THE ULTIMATE

BRITNEY SPEARS

QUIZ BOOK

MAGGIE MARRON

MetroBooks

MetroBooks

An Imprint of Friedman/Fairfax Publishers

©2000 by Michael Friedman Publishing Group, Inc.

Library of Congress Cataloging-in-Publication Data

Marron, Maggie.
    The ultimate Britney Spears quiz book / Maggie Marron.
        p. cm.
Includes bibliographical references and index.
ISBN 1-58663-136-5 (alk. paper)
    1. Spears, Britney—Miscellanea 2. Singers—United States—Miscellanea.
ML420.S714 M37 2000
782.42164'092—dc21
[B]

00-063631

Editor: Dan Heend
Art Director: Kevin Ullrich
Designers: Mark Weinberg
Photo Editor: Jami Ruszkai
Production Manager: Richela Fabian Morgan

Color separations by Bright Arts Graphics (S) Pte. Ltd.
Printed in the U.S.A. by R.R. Donnelley & Sons Co.

1 3 5 7 9 10 8 6 4 2

For bulk purchases and special sales, please contact:
Friedman/Fairfax Publishers
Attention: Sales Department
15 West 26th Street
New York, NY 10010
212/685-6610 FAX 212/685-1307

Visit our website:
www.metrobooks.com

Dedication

For Raoul Duke

Acknowledgments

This book could not be possible without all the Britney fans out there—thanks for loving the reigning princess of pop as much as I do! And thanks to everyone who made this book possible, especially to researcher extraordinaire Christine Guarino Mayer, who spent countless hours sifting through everything there is to know about Britney Spears—and who helped put together some of the quizzes. Also, a ton of thanks to my editor, Dan Heend, for signing me up for the project and for being such a good sport. Last but not least, thanks to my good pal and mentor, Francine Hornberger, who has always helped me find just the right words to write all of my books.

Bio

A New York-based freelance writer and editor, Maggie Marron is the author of several pictorial celebrity biographies, including *Britney Spears: Stylin', Ricky Martin, The Backstreet Boys, Will Smith: From Rap Star to Mega Star,* and *Christina Aguilera: The Unauthorized Biography* as well as *The Ultimate Backstreet Boys Quiz Book* and *The Ultimate 'N SYNC Quiz Book.* She has also written for *Kickin'* magazine and profiled numerous celebrities for *People* Magazine Online. Write to Maggie with your comments and suggestions for books about your favorite stars at maggiemarron@chickmail.com.

Contents

Introduction

Britney Spears took the pop music world by storm at the end of 1998 when she came out with her first number one hit, "…Baby, One More Time." Since then, Britney's been everywhere—from the radio and MTV to countless ads for everything from shampoo to milk. And still, we just can't get enough! That combination of raw talent, impeccable style, natural beauty, a gracious and sweet nature, and killer drive is what makes Britney a star and keeps us wanting more and more! Well, here's more.

Welcome to *The Ultimate Britney Spears Quiz Book*. Here's how it works. Each of the initial sixteen quizzes has fifteen questions for you to answer, which range from seemingly easy to truly baffling. The questions are about everything from Britney's favorite things to her family life, her music, and her superstardom. And the questions are purposely random—so you can't rely on knowing the subject of the quiz to find the answers. All of the quizzes include special questions that are worth extra points if you answer them correctly. You'll add up and record your points at the end of each quiz, and then move right on to the next challenge.

There are side stories throughout where you may find an answer or two, but basically you'll have to rely on what you already know! After you've completed sixteen quizzes, you'll find a bonus quiz where you can pick up more points in the race to prove that you are *the* ultimate Britney Spears fan. At the end of the book you'll add up your total points and see how informed a Britney fan you really are!

Good luck! Now, put on your favorite Brit CD and turn to the first quiz … on your mark, get set, go!

Love, Maggie

Britney even makes fringe look stylin'.

8

Quiz 1

1. **What's the biggest city closest to Britney's hometown?**
a. New Orleans
b. San Francisco
c. Birmingham
d. Nashville

2. **Britney's sun sign is:**
a. Cancer
b. Sagittarius
c. Taurus
d. Leo

3. **Which of these is one of Britney's nicknames?**
a. Brit-meister
b. Brit-Brit
c. Brit-a-rooney
d. Brit-ski

4. **Which of these musical acts does Britney love to listen to the most?**
a. Michael Jackson
b. Whitney Houston
c. Prince
d. All of the above

5. **Which of the following would be Brit's dream date?**
a. Ben Affleck
b. Edward Norton
c. Ricky Martin
d. Eminem

She's talented, hard-working—and lucky!

challenge Begins

6. How tall is Britney?

a. 5'0"

b. 5'2"

c. 5'4"

d. 5'6"

7. Britney's second album is titled:

a. *Oops!...I Did It Again*

b. *Oh no!...Not Again*

c. *Oops!...I Made a New Friend*

d. *Oops!...Will It Ever End???*

8. Which TGIF star appears in Britney's video for "Crazy"?

a. Danielle Fishel

b. Melissa Joan Hart

c. The guys from O-Town

d. Matthew Lawrence

9. In the first part of the video for "...Baby, One More Time," Britney is wearing a:

a. Basketball uniform

b. Clown suit

c. School uniform

d. Cat suit

10. Britney's fave actress is:

a. Meg Ryan

b. Neve Campbell

c. Elizabeth Hurley

d. Jennifer Love Hewitt

11. Which of the following does Britney enjoy as a hobby:

a. Shopping

b. Going to movies

c. Riding her go-cart

d. All of the above

12. Which is Britney's soda of choice?

a. Sprite

b. Ginger ale

c. Coke

d. Mountain Dew

13. Brit's favorite movie is:

a. *Gone With the Wind*

b. *American Beauty*

c. *Loser*

d. *Steel Magnolias*

14. Britney doesn't get to watch a lot of TV, but when she does, she makes sure never to miss her favorite sit-com:

a. *Will and Grace*

b. *Friends*

c. *Sabrina, the Teenage Witch*

d. *Boy Meets World*

15. Brit's favorite basketball player is:

a. Michael Jordan

b. Allan Houston

c. Shaq

d. Scottie Pippen

ANSWERS

1. a
2. b
3. b
4. d
5. a
6. c
7. a
8. b
9. c
10. a
11. d
12. a
13. d
14. b
15. a

SCORING

*Give yourself one point for every
question you answered correctly.
Now, give yourself **three extra points**
for each correct answer to questions
1, 8, and 13.*

QUIZ #1 SCORE: _____

Britney and dancers in the "Sometimes" video.

Britney Spears: Heart of Gold

Well, we all know how talented Britney Spears is. And we all know how beautiful and stylish she is. And there's no question that she's a really nice person—but do you know just *how* nice she is? Even with so many hours spent recording, making videos, and touring, Britney has still managed to find time to work with charities and give something back. Incredible! So just what is Britney doing with her spare time these days?

In July 2000, Britney Spears was named the official spokesperson for the Starlight Children's Foundation. Starlight's mission is to brighten the lives of seriously ill children by granting a special wish. Some children request meeting a favorite celebrity, while others might want to go someplace they've always wanted to see, like Disney World. Starlight does whatever it can to make these wishes come true.

Part of what Britney's done for the foundation is to establish signature playrooms in hospitals throughout the country. The first of these playrooms was launched at Chicago's Shriners Hospital for Children in July.

And as if that's not enough, Britney has created her own foundation and joined up with the Giving Back Fund to establish a performing-arts summer camp. The camp gives eighty-five inner-city children, ages eleven to fourteen, the opportunity to attend performing arts workshops for nine summer days in the Berkshire Hills in Massachusetts. Instructors include Britney's choreographer, a singing instructor—even Britney herself will make an appearance! Kids are chosen based on economic need and interest in the performing arts.

Get Involved

Do you want to make a difference like Britney? Contact these charities to see what you can do to help:

STARLIGHT CHILDREN'S FOUNDATION
(International Headquarters)
5900 Wilshire Blvd., Suite 2530
Los Angeles, CA 90036
323-634-0080 (phone)
323-634-0090 (fax)
info@starlight.org (email)

**THE GIVING BACK FUND /
THE BRITNEY SPEARS FOUNDATION**
54 Canal Street
Suite 320
Boston, MA 02114
617-557-9910 (phone)
617-973-9463 (fax)
giveback@ma.ultranet.com (email)

Beautiful, talented, and big-hearted—what a combo!

Britney: Fact or Fiction?

Quiz 2

1. Britney Spears was born on December 5, 1981.

2. Britney has a rottweiler named Cane.

3. Britney's mother's name is Jamie.

4. Britney is the oldest child in her family.

5. Britney has big, beautiful, blue eyes.

6. Britney can't get enough of chocolate chip, cookie dough ice cream.

7. Britney originally wanted the video for "...Baby, One More Time" to be a "cartoonish space-rangers kind of thing."

8. Britney was not nervous at all when she filmed the "...Baby, One More Time" video.

9. Britney's favorite author is Danielle Steel.

10. Britney loves to wear Tommy Hilfiger clothes.

11. Britney loves to watch Brad Pitt on the big screen.

12. Britney modeled clothing for Versace's Spring 1999 collection.

13. Britney started dance lessons at age seven.

14. Britney used to perform at shopping malls.

15. Britney wrote the song "Sometimes" from her first album.

Part 1

Britney Spears, ball girl.

ANSWERS

1. Fiction. She was born on December 2.

2. Fact.

3. Fiction. That's her dad! Her mom's name is Lynne, natch!

4. Fiction. She's right smack in the middle between Bryan and Jamie Lynn.

5. Fiction. While Britney no doubt has big and beautiful eyes, they are definitely brown!

6. Fact.

7. Fiction. Britney thought she would look like a fool if she did it that way. Actually, it was Britney who suggested the concept that stuck.

8. Oh so fictional! Britney was a nervous wreck. But she ended up having a lot of fun because there was a lot of dancing involved and she is an excellent dancer!

9. Fact.

10. Fact.

11. Fact.

12. Fiction. It was for Tommy Hilfiger.

13. Fiction. Britney put on her dancing shoes at age four—and has yet to take them off!

14. Fact.

15. Fiction. But she did write "I'm So Curious," which appears on the flip side of the "Sometimes" single.

SCORING

*Give yourself one point for every question you answered correctly. Now, give yourself **three extra points** each if you got 1, 7, and 12 right.*

QUIZ #2 SCORE: _____

Brit accepts an award from her *NSYNC pals.

Quiz 3

Hip huggers and a halter top—now that's Britney style!

NEXT HURDLE

1. **How old was Britney when she was signed to Jive Records?**
a. Twelve
b. Thirteen
c. Fifteen
d. Seventeen

2. **What was the first boy band Britney toured with?**
a. Backstreet Boys
b. *NSYNC
c. 98°
d. Five

3. **Who is Britney's best friend?**
a. Christina Aguilera
b. Her sister, Jamie Lynn
c. Her mama
d. Justin Timberlake

4. **What did Britney collect as a child?**
a. Pez dispensers
b. Dolls
c. Paper clips
d. Barbie shoes

5. **Britney's guardian's name is:**
a. Felicia Spears
b. Felicia Culotta
c. Pina Culotta
d. Felicia Finklestein

6. **Which TGIF show did Britney make an appearance on?**
a. *Two of a Kind*
b. *Sabrina, the Teenage Witch*
c. *Boy Meets World*
d. *Making the Band*

7. **What's the estimated population of Britney's hometown?**
a. 500
b. 2,600
c. 3,500
d. 5,000

8. **Where did Britney grow up?**
a. Rosemont, IL
b. Little Rock, AR
c. Kentwood, LA
d. Staten Island, NY

9. **In what grade did Britney leave school to pursue her career?**
a. Fourth grade
b. Seventh grade
c. Ninth grade
d. Tenth grade

10. **What's Brit's favorite song from her first album?**
a. "Soda Pop"
b. "...Baby, One More Time"
c. "The Beat Goes On"
d. "E-mail My Heart"

11. **Who is Britney's manager?**
a. Larry Rudolph
b. Johnny Wright
c. Both Larry and Johnny
d. Lynne Spears

12. **Who are Britney's fashion icons?**
a. Madonna and Mariah Carey
b. Jennifer Aniston and Jennifer Love Hewitt
c. Christina Aguilera and Gwen Stefani
d. Cher and Janet Jackson

13. **What are the three words Britney most uses to describe herself?**
a. Honest, trustworthy, and sweet
b. Cutthroat, ambitious, and selfish
c. Talented, beautiful, and famous
d. Curious, mischievous, and creative

14. **What did Britney wear in her 1999 Disney special?**
a. A pink crop top and white pants
b. A gold lamé gown
c. A black leather jumpsuit
d. An orange fake-fur jacket over a plastic fuchsia gown

15. **How long was Britney a Mouseketeer?**
a. One season
b. Two seasons
c. Three seasons
d. Four seasons

ANSWERS

1. c
2. b
3. c
4. b
5. b
6. b
7. b
8. c
9. c
10. b
11. c
12. b
13. a
14. a
15. b

SCORING

*Give yourself one point for every question you answered correctly. Now, give yourself **three extra points** each if you got 4, 9, and 13 right.*

QUIZ #3 SCORE: _____

Who wouldn't want to take the glamorous Ms. Spears to the prom?

Brit belts out a serious tune.

Mama Mia!

When Brian Littrell wrote the song "The Perfect Fan" for his own mom, did he realize how many of his fellow pop stars have also been able to come as far as they have because of the love and support of their own mothers?

If it wasn't for her mom's belief in her, would we know the name Christina Aguilera today? Shelly Kearns took Christina on all the rounds, from local talent shows to *Star Search* to Orlando for the *All-New Mickey Mouse Club*. And Christina wasn't the only one feeling the backlash of her burgeoning stardom wherever they lived. Poor Shelly was ostracized by the other parents—and even had her tires slashed—all because they were jealous of Christina's career. "As soon as *Star Search* happened, a lot of my mom's friends, other parents, wouldn't talk to us anymore," Christina has told *Teen People*. But Shelly never gave up on her daughter, and thank goodness for that! Christina and Shelly are best friends. In fact, every time she sings "I Turn to You," she always thinks of her mom.

And what about the boys? Well, because of Jane Carter, we get to know the real truth about Backstreet Boy Nick and his adorable younger brother Aaron. Jane is the author of two books each on both of her famous sons! She's always done whatever she can to make sure they follow their dreams—even moving from New York to Florida. And her magic mothering really seems to be working, as there's a new pop star emerging from the Carter family—Nick and Aaron's little sister Leslie!

A.J. McLean's mom also moved herself and her son to Orlando so A.J. could have a chance at fame. Denise McLean always encouraged her son to follow his show-business dreams, and when he found his ticket with the Backstreet Boys, she even became the group's publicist!

Of course we know who Britney's biggest fan is. And Britney's mom is also her daughter's best friend. From pageants to talent shows to dance lessons to gymnastics, Lynne Spears has always given Britney the support she needed to realize her dreams. She truly is the perfect fan!

Britney and her mom, Lynne Spears.

Britney: Fact or Fiction?

Quiz 4

1. Britney loves Nirvana and would rather sing grunge than pop music.

2. Britney has to talk to her mama every single day.

3. Britney hurt her knee while filming the video for "Crazy."

4. Britney made it onto the cast of the *All-New Mickey Mouse Club* the first time she auditioned for the show.

5. Britney is a morning person.

6. As a child Britney loved to have make-believe concerts using her stuffed animals and dolls as the audience.

7. Britney admires Madonna for the way she always reinvents herself.

8. Britney is produced by Lou Pearlman.

9. Britney won an award for Best New Pop Recording Artist at the Grammys.

10. Britney had a miserable childhood.

11. Britney wears a beaded gown in the video for "Sometimes."

12. Britney hated acting in *MMC* and never wants to do it again.

13. In the video for "Crazy," Britney changes from a green half tank top and tight black sparkly pants into a waitress uniform.

14. Britney's hometown is building a museum in her honor.

15. Britney performed at the tree-lighting ceremony at Rockefeller Plaza in 1999.

Part 2

Britney Spears, all-American beauty.

ANSWERS

1. Fiction. While she may or may not have a Nirvana CD in her collection, Brit feels that pop music suits her best and plans to stick to it.

2. Fact.

3. Fiction. She did hurt her knee, but it was while filming "Sometimes," her second single.

4. Fiction. While that audition got the attention of the producers, they told her she was too young. They called her back soon enough, though!

5. Way fiction. Britney says that her voice doesn't wake up until around noon.

6. Fact.

7. Fact.

8. Fiction. Max Martin produces Britney.

9. Fiction. She did win at the American Music Awards, however. It was pop diva-ette Christina Aguilera who swiped the Grammy.

10. Totally fiction! Brit had a great childhood. Her family didn't have a lot of money, but there was always plenty of love to go around!

11. Fiction. She wears a long white dress throughout the video—but never a beaded gown. Imagine wearing a number like that to the beach! Tacky!

12. Fiction. Britney is actually dying to make a movie—she's just waiting for the perfect project to come along.

13. Fiction—it's the other way around!

14. Fact.

15. Fact.

SCORING

*Give yourself one point for every question you answered correctly. Now, give yourself **three extra points** each if you got 5, 8, and 13 right.*

QUIZ #4 SCORE: _____

Britney and her dancers get down and dirty in concert.

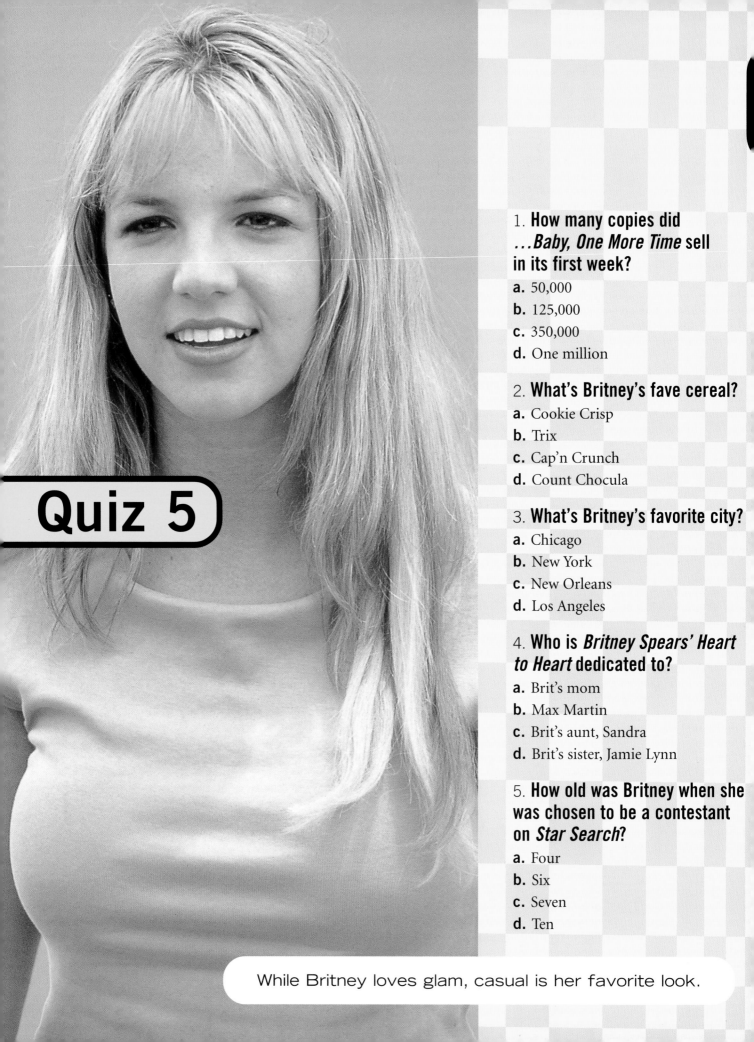

Quiz 5

1. **How many copies did ...*Baby, One More Time* sell in its first week?**
   a. 50,000
   b. 125,000
   c. 350,000
   d. One million

2. **What's Britney's fave cereal?**
   a. Cookie Crisp
   b. Trix
   c. Cap'n Crunch
   d. Count Chocula

3. **What's Britney's favorite city?**
   a. Chicago
   b. New York
   c. New Orleans
   d. Los Angeles

4. **Who is *Britney Spears' Heart to Heart* dedicated to?**
   a. Brit's mom
   b. Max Martin
   c. Brit's aunt, Sandra
   d. Brit's sister, Jamie Lynn

5. **How old was Britney when she was chosen to be a contestant on *Star Search*?**
   a. Four
   b. Six
   c. Seven
   d. Ten

While Britney loves glam, casual is her favorite look.

Keeping Up the Pace

6. How many record labels turned Britney down before Jive picked her up?

a. One

b. Two

c. Four

d. Seven

7. Where did Britney first start taking dance lessons?

a. The Kentwood School for the Arts

b. The Kentwood Academy

c. The Renee Donewar School of Dance

d. The Sandy Duncan School of Dance

8. Which of the following competitions did Britney win as a child?

a. Miss Talent Central States Competition

b. The Little Miss America Competition

c. The *Dance Fever* Junior Competition

d. The All-American Girl Talent Competition

9. What's Britney's favorite breakfast food?

a. Brown-sugar flavored oatmeal

b. Eggs Benedict

c. Silver-dollar pancakes with chocolate syrup

d. Scrambled eggs with plenty of ketchup

10. What did Jive Records present to Britney for her eighteenth birthday?

a. A five-record deal

b. A brand-new Porsche

c. A penthouse apartment in New York City

d. A diamond necklace

11. If Britney goes to college, what does she want to study?

a. Entertainment law

b. Psychology

c. English lit.

d. Religion

12. What's Britney's perfect date?

a. A romantic ride in a hot-air balloon

b. Dancing until dawn

c. Dinner and a movie

d. A horse and buggy ride through the park

13. Max Martin has also produced albums for:

a. The Backstreet Boys

b. Ace of Base

c. Both a and b

d. Neither a nor b

14. What is Britney's religion?

a. Baptist

b. Unitarian

c. Methodist

d. Catholic

15. When did the single "…Baby, One More Time" hit stores?

a. October 16, 1998

b. October 23, 1998

c. November 1, 1998

d. January 4, 1999

ANSWERS

1. b
2. c
3. a
4. c
5. d
6. b
7. c
8. a
9. b
10. d
11. a
12. c
13. c
14. a
15. b

SCORING

*Give yourself one point for every question you answered correctly. Now, give yourself **three extra points** each if you got 1, 5, and 11 right.*

QUIZ #5 SCORE: _____

Britney started dance lessons at age four.

FAME: Is It Everything

Any famous person will tell you that the price of fame is high—and the more famous you are, the bigger the bill. When you reach a certain pinnacle, your every move is monitored, and instead of just being who you are, you become a role model, a piece of property that people think they own. Britney knows this only too well.

When she was asked if her song "Lucky" had any relation to her life she replied, "Yes, definitely. Everyone thinks you're having a 'whoop-de-do' time, but if you're really serious about your music you can't just play all the time."

On top of all the hard work, Britney can't go anywhere these days and not be recognized. She says, "Usually when I go into a mall it's kind of overbearing sometimes. I usually try to disguise myself." She remembers the last time she didn't take the time to put together a good disguise: "Stupid, stupid!" says Britney. "All of a sudden people all over the mall are looking at me. The whole [store] entrance was backed up with people! It was overwhelming. A lot of times I forget that I'm a celebrity."

One of the hardest things about being a celebrity is that the public watches your every move and is very critical of everything you do, which she found out the hard way when she did her now-infamous photo shoot for *Rolling Stone.* "When I saw the cover I thought 'wow, this is hot,'" says Britney, "but I guess other people thought it was too sexy." Britney got a lot of backlash from that shoot, including a boycott from the Mississippi-based American Family Association organization, which really shocked her. "I'm not going to walk around in hot pants and a bra on the street," she explained, "but when you're an artist you sometimes play a part."

Luckily, Britney has a lot of celebrity pals she can talk to. Her good friend Melissa Joan Hart had a similar experience with her *Maxim* exposé, and Britney says they would discuss the topic on the phone together. Both women decided that they would stand by their decisions to take those photos, no matter what. You go, girls!

Despite her fame, Britney prefers to live a normal teenage life—at least as normal as she can. "I don't live a completely normal life because I'm not, you know, a typical teenager who goes to school every day," she told *Teen Magazine* in August of 1999. "But I try to make it as normal as possible." All in all, Britney finds stardom "very flattering." She says, "it's really nice having so many people look up to you."

Fame has a price, as Brit and her pal Melissa Joan Hart (left) both found out the hard way

It's Cracked Up To Be?

Britney: Fact or Fiction?

Quiz 6

1. Britney had a falling out with her cousin Laura Lynne when she was ten years old and has not spoken to her since.

2. The first time Lynne Spears heard one of Britney's songs on the radio, she ran outside and screamed for joy in the middle of the street.

3. Britney's debut album ...*Baby, One More Time* has sold more than twelve million copies!

4. Britney Spears has a video called *Dining Out with Britney Spears*.

5. Britney Spears is the first female and youngest artist ever to have a simultaneous number-one debut album and single.

6. ...*Baby, One More Time* reached certified gold, platinum, and double-platinum status simultaneously.

7. While Britney enjoys fame, she worries that becoming too famous could cause her to lose her identity and her privacy.

8. Britney's aunt Sandra is battling lung cancer.

9. Britney used to be afraid of Santa Claus.

10. Britney lost her *Star Search* competition to Christina Aguilera.

11. Miss Britney Spears was once crowned Miss Talent USA.

12. Britney says that her time with *MMC* taught her how to get what she wanted at any cost.

13. Britney's mama thinks she is an excellent driver.

14. As a child, Britney used to give herself dance report cards after a performance.

15. Britney loves to fly.

Part 3

Girlfriend's on fire—or at least that's what her top looks like!

ANSWERS

1. Fiction! Fiction! Fiction! In fact, Britney considers Laura Lynne one of her very best friends.

2. While that would be funny if it were true, Lynne's first reaction was to burst out crying. In fact, she couldn't stop crying—with happiness, of course!

3. Fact! Fact! Fact!—and then some!

4. Fiction, you silly head! It's called *Time Out With Britney Spears*!

5. Fact.

6. Fact.

7. Fact.

8. Fiction. It's ovarian cancer.

9. Fact.

10. Fiction. As if!

11. Fact.

12. Fiction. The cast of *MMC* was really close and Britney has said that, if anything, the experience taught her how to be a team player.

13. Fiction. Lynne says that other drivers are constantly honking at them on the road when Britney drives—and it's not to say hello, if you know what I mean!

14. Fact.

15. Fiction. Britney's really scared every time she's in an airplane. Air travel is the one thing she's never gotten used to in her hectic life.

SCORING

*Give yourself one point for every question you answered correctly. Now, give yourself **three extra points** each if you got 4, 8, and 13 right.*

QUIZ #6 SCORE: _____

Brit takes a moment to sample some tunes at a record store's listening station.

Quiz 7

Finish

that Line—Part 1

1. "My loneliness is killing me (and I), I must confess I still believe (still believe)..."

2. "Every time you look at me, My heart is jumpin', it's easy to see..."

3. "I know I've been a fool since you've been gone, I'd better give it up and carry on (oh my love)..."

4. "Won't you let me make it up to you, Now you know where I am..."

5. "I can see you in my mind, Coming on the line..."

6. "Red leaves and blue tomorrows, Time will give back the love that we shared..."

7. "From now until forever..."

8. "It might seem like a crush, But it doesn't mean that I'm serious..."

9. "You got no reasons to be jealous, I've never been untrue..."

10. "Dear Diary, Dear Diary, Today I saw a boy and I wondered if he noticed me..."

11. "My friends say you're so into me..."

12. "Calling out your name, Your face is everywhere..."

13. "There's a girl in the mirror. I wonder who she is..."

14. "There's a kindred spirit that's thrilling to see..."

15. "I have been through changes, yeah. But I'm still the girl you used to know..."

Hey, Britney—is that a tattoo?

ANSWERS

1. "…When I'm not with you I lose my mind, Give me a sign, hit me baby, one more time" ("…Baby, One More Time")

2. "…Lovin' you means so much more, More than anything I ever felt before" ("Crazy")

3. "…'Cause living in a dream of you and me, Is not the way my life should be" ("Born to Make You Happy")

4. "…There ain't nothing that I wouldn't do, Just to love once again" ("I Will Be There")

5. "…And opening this letter, That I've sent a hundred times" ("E-mail My Heart")

6. "…On the time that we borrowed" ("Autumn Goodbye")

7. "…that's how long I'll be true" ("I'll Never Stop Loving You")

8. "…'Cause to lose all my senses, That is just so typically me" ("Oops!… I Did It Again")

9. "…So does it really matter if they're looking, I'm only looking at you" ("What You See [Is What You Get]")

10. "…He took my breath away" ("Dear Diary")

11. "…And that you need me desperately" ("Don't Let Me Be the Last to Know")

12. "…I'm reaching out to you, To find that you're not there" ("Where Are You Now?")

13. "…Sometimes I think I know her, Sometimes I really wish I did" ("Girl In the Mirror")

14. "…The closeness that we feel—it's so fulfilling to me" ("My Little Star," Lynne Spears' poem about Britney, the toddler)

15. "…It's made me no different, So tell me why you had to go" ("Can't Make You Love Me")

SCORING

*Give yourself one point for every question you answered correctly. Now, give yourself **three extra points** each if you got 4, 9, and 14 right.*

QUIZ #7 SCORE: _____

"Sometimes" all a girl needs is a little quiet time.

Britney's winning smile has clinched endorsement deals with Clairol and Polaroid, among others.

Britney considers her dancers to be family and is always confident performing when they're around.

Britney Spears is the first gal to tell you that she couldn't have gotten this far without the help and support of the people in her life that are the closest to her. Who are the special people in Britney's life?

Number one, bar none, is her mother, Lynne Spears. Without Lynne's scrimping and saving whatever money the Spears family had to give Britney the lessons she needed, and without her undying love and encouragement, Britney might just be the most talented person in Kentwood, Louisiana—and no one would know her anywhere else! In the introduction to the book she wrote with her mother, *Heart to Heart*, Britney explains that there are three important keys to success: "(1) talent, (2) belief in yourself, and (3) someone who believes in you. My mama was that person." And on top of having a good mother-daughter relationship, Britney and her mama are very close friends. As Lynne explains, "We've always managed to put any differences aside and focus on what is the key to any good relationship—love and respect for each other."

Britney doesn't talk about her dad much, though she does respect his suggestions. When Britney was offered a role in the film *Gordy*, Jamie Spears encouraged her to go for it. It was difficult for her to stand up for what she really wanted, but she had to follow her heart. Soon enough, *MMC* finally called and Britney was primed and ready to jump right in to the soon-to-be-all-star lineup. Oh well, dad. Better luck next time!

Like every big brother, Bryan Spears is mega-protective of his little sis—even if he didn't always let it show. Come on. What big brother lets his little sister know that she's anything but a pain in the neck? But Bryan has always looked out for Britney. "In school all these boys were wanting to ask her out,

My Friends…And Family!

but they had to get not just Daddy's approval, but mine as well." That doesn't mean he doesn't relish his role as head torturer of Britney Spears, however. "Whenever she comes home, it's the same Britney. We fight. I'm the only person who knows what to say to get her real steamed—and that's fun."

Britney describes the day her little sister was born as the most memorable in her life. And little Jamie Lynn thinks her big sis is the moon and the stars. "She is so cool," Jamie coos in *Heart to Heart*, "and she's a really good singer. When I grow up, I'm gonna be just like her." There's no rivalry on Britney's part. In fact, she'd love for her baby sister to be as famous as she is. "She's the sweetest kid," Britney has beamed, "and I just know she's going to be a big star herself one day."

Britney doesn't have a big sister by blood, but she's found a surrogate in her guardian Felicia Culotta, who is also one of her best friends. Fe, as Brit calls her, is even featured in one of Britney's videos! She plays the schoolteacher in "…Baby, One More Time." And Fe can't get enough of her "little sister": "I'm lucky enough to know her better than most…" she explains in *Heart to Heart*. And Britney says: "I feel like she [Fe] is my right arm, and I don't know what I'd do without her in my life."

Laura Lynn Covington is just a few months younger than her larger-than-life pal and cousin, Britney Spears, and over the years, through thick and thin, they've been totally inseparable. There's no jealousy. No power struggles. No swelled head on Britney's shoulders. "To me, she's just Britney," Laura Lynn explains. "She doesn't put on any airs or act differently, even though her life has changed so much these past few years."

In addition to being the mother of Britney's closest friend, her aunt Sandra is also one of the most inspiring people she knows. Britney is in awe of her strength in her battle with ovarian cancer. And the feeling is basically mutual. "Have you heard about my niece?" Sandra declares. "Isn't she amazing?"

Britney is grateful to have her producers, managers, and dancers as a second family, and says, "You don't have to be kin to care about one another."

Last and far from being least, Britney has relied on God and her faith to take her to the dazzling heights she's achieved. Throughout everything, she has never lost her faith. "I pray all the time. Every night before I go to sleep," she says.

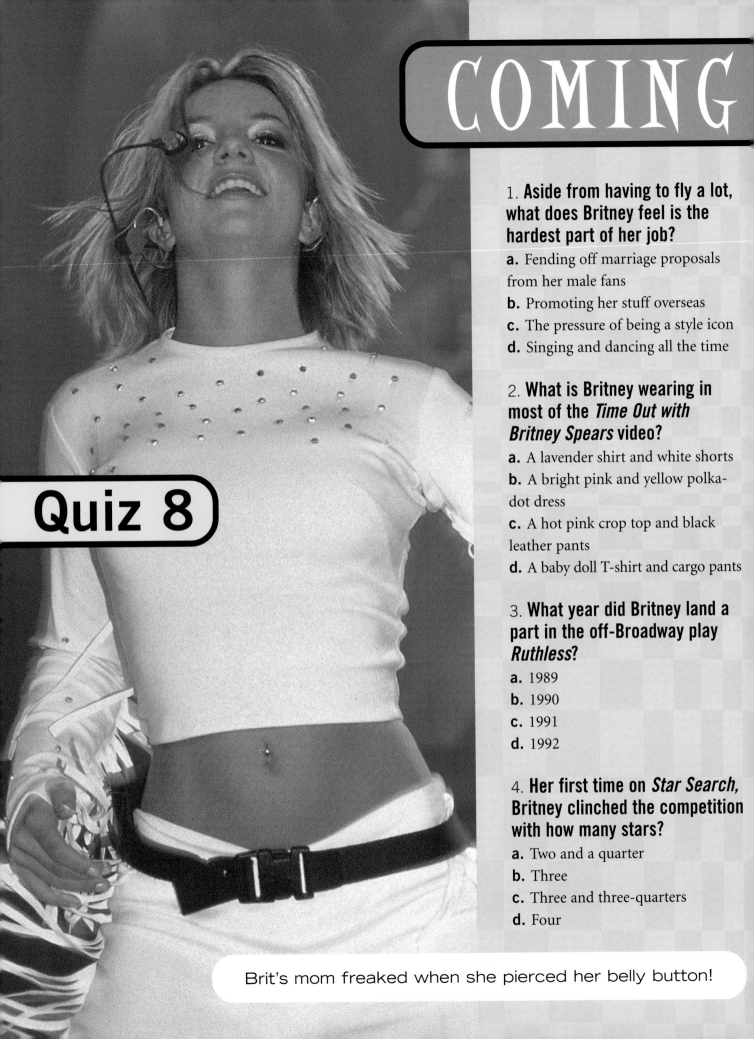

COMING

Quiz 8

1. **Aside from having to fly a lot, what does Britney feel is the hardest part of her job?**
   a. Fending off marriage proposals from her male fans
   b. Promoting her stuff overseas
   c. The pressure of being a style icon
   d. Singing and dancing all the time

2. **What is Britney wearing in most of the *Time Out with Britney Spears* video?**
   a. A lavender shirt and white shorts
   b. A bright pink and yellow polka-dot dress
   c. A hot pink crop top and black leather pants
   d. A baby doll T-shirt and cargo pants

3. **What year did Britney land a part in the off-Broadway play *Ruthless*?**
   a. 1989
   b. 1990
   c. 1991
   d. 1992

4. **Her first time on *Star Search*, Britney clinched the competition with how many stars?**
   a. Two and a quarter
   b. Three
   c. Three and three-quarters
   d. Four

Brit's mom freaked when she pierced her belly button!

5. Britney's opponent for her first *Star Search* competition sang in which of the following styles:

a. Country and western

b. Rock 'n' roll

c. Gospel

d. Opera

6. What did Britney sing for her second appearance on *Star Search*?

a. Olivia Newton-John's "Hopelessly Devoted to You"

b. Naomi Judd's "Love Can Build a Bridge"

c. Nena's "99 Red Balloons"

d. Madonna's "Lucky Star"

7. When Britney found out she lost the *Star Search* competition, she:

a. Stormed off the stage

b. Cried her eyes out

c. Threw a tomato at the winner

d. Swore she would quit showbiz forever

8. What was the first song Britney ever sang for a public audience?

a. "What Child Is This"

b. "The Itsy-Bitsy Spider"

c. "Twinkle, Twinkle Little Star"

d. "I'm a Little Teapot"

9. Before her second *Star Search* performance, Britney:

a. Practiced her scales in her dressing room

b. Went shopping to clear her mind

c. Played basketball with the boy who would defeat her

d. Went for ice cream with her mama

10. Which special person in Brit's life appeared in her "…Baby, One More Time" video?

a. Her mother, Lynne

b. Her guardian, Fe

c. Her brother, Bryan

d. Her manager, Johnny Wright

11. When did Britney win her first competition?

a. 1986

b. 1987

c. 1989

d. 1990

12. How long did Britney spend in Sweden recording her first album?

a. Nearly a month

b. Just over six months

c. Almost a year

d. More than two years

13. Which song won Britney the 1992 Miss Talent USA competition?

a. "There, I've Said It Again"

b. "You've Got It All Over Him"

c. "I Will Always Love You"

d. "Once in a Lifetime"

14. What was the name of the all-girl band Britney was in for one day before signing with Jive Records?

a. B*witched

b. Innosense

c. Eternal

d. Candy Girls

15. Who manages the all-girl band that Britney almost joined?

a. Brian Littrell of the Backstreet Boys

b. Jane Carter, Nick Carter's mother

c. JC Chasez of *NSYNC

d. Lynne Harless, Justin Timberlake's mother

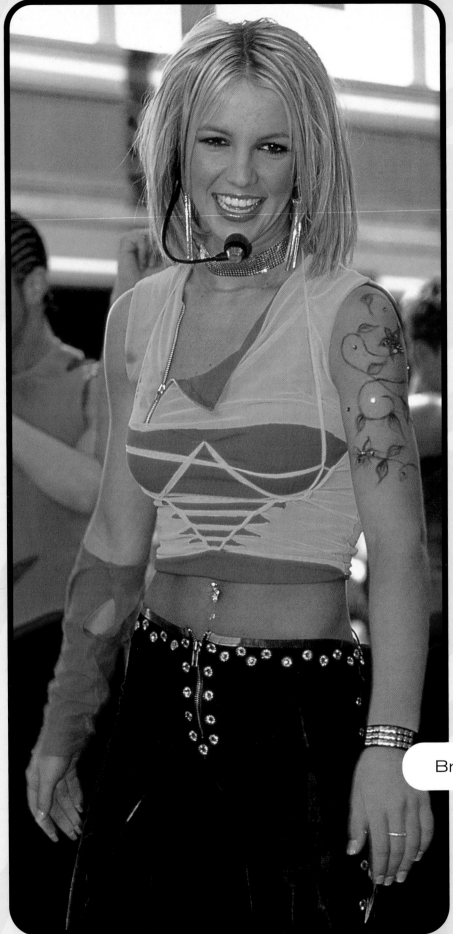

ANSWERS

1. b
2. a
3. c
4. c
5. d
6. b
7. b
8. a
9. c
10. b
11. d
12. c
13. a
14. b
15. d

SCORING

*Give yourself one point for every question you answered correctly. Now, give yourself **three extra points** each if you got 2, 5, and 12 right.*

QUIZ #8 SCORE: _____

Brit can pull off short hair...

...or long! She always looks beautiful!

Britney: Fact or Fiction?

Quiz 9

1. Britney is a party animal.

2. Britney likes old blues music.

3. Britney won first place in the Kentwood Dairy Festival.

4. Britney's mom, Lynne, wrote a poem about Britney called "My Little Flower."

5. Britney initially signed an unlimited contract with Jive Records.

6. Britney writes in a prayer journal every night.

7. The first foreign country Britney ever visited was England.

8. Britney has never sung a duet with Justin Timberlake.

9. On June 30, 2000, Britney's performance on *The Today Show* drew the largest crowd to date in the history of the show: more than 6,000 fans!

10. The transformation of dorky waitress to sexy singing babe in Britney's "Crazy" video was her mother Lynne's idea.

11. Britney had several serious boyfriends in high school.

12. Britney never really liked her hometown—and stardom was her way out.

13. Before Britney goes on stage she likes to pray with her dancers.

14. The *National Enquirer* started the rumor that Britney was engaged to her pal Justin Timberlake.

15. Britney played Tina, the lead, in *Ruthless*, her first off-Broadway play.

Part 4

Brit's brother, Bryan, was very protective of his little sis when they were growing up—can you blame him?!?

ANSWERS

1. Fiction. She's really not into partying at all. She says she would rather "take a hot bubble bath and get a good night's sleep."

2. Fact.

3. Fact.

4. Fiction. Mom wrote a poem titled "My Little Star."

5. Fiction. Actually, when Brit first signed on with Jive, they had a ninety-day out clause, meaning if Britney didn't prove herself in ninety days, she'd be pounding the pavement for a new label.

6. Fact.

7. Fiction. When Britney was signed to Jive, she was sent to Sweden to work with Max Martin.

8. Fiction. On *MMC* Britney sang "I Feel For You" with Justin.

9. Fact.

10. Fiction. That cool concept came right from Britney herself!

11. Fiction. Britney says that when she recorded songs about love such as "From the Bottom of My Broken Heart" she hadn't experienced all of the emotions she was singing about because she had only one serious boyfriend while in school.

12. Fiction. While her stardom keeps her away from home a lot, Brit loves everything about her hometown—except that everybody knows everybody else's business!

13. Fact.

14. Fiction. The *Enquirer* is innocent this time! It was the British tabloid, *News of the World,* that started that doozy.

15. Fact. At first Britney was cast as the understudy for the lead, but when the star left, she actually played the lead for six months.

SCORING

*Give yourself one point for every question you answered correctly. Now, give yourself **three extra points** each if you got 4, 10, and 15 right.*

QUIZ #9 SCORE: _____

Take a bow, girlfriend!

Matchmaker, Matchmaker

Britney never has time to date, but she says her perfect boyfriend is "a guy that has a wonderful personality and can make me laugh and has a lot of confidence. I find that very sexy." Let's play big sister for Britney. If we could fix her up with anyone, who would it be? Well, Brit's so cute, she could make any suitor look better just by being with him. But who would she make a really cute couple with?

By now we're all bored to death by the rumors that Britney's romantically involved with Justin Timberlake. Well, while they'd no doubt make an adorable couple, there may be at least one *NSYNC'er that Britney would be cuter with. How about dreamboat **JC Chasez**, who's also pals with Britney from their time on *MMC*? JC's piercing eyes and velvety-smooth voice plus Brit's puppy-dog eyes and sexy vocal stylings: now there's a couple! And although JC has never come out and expressed interest in Britney—no doubt he's trying to avoid becoming another faux fiancé—he's had only sweet things to say about her. "Guys are into her because she's cute, and girls like her because she's not trying too hard," he told *People Weekly* way back in May of 1999.

Speaking of rumors, what about that whopper about Britney being involved with **Prince William**? Well, would that really be the worst thing if Britney fell in love with the handsome prince? He's adorable. He's sweet. And he's got his mother's looks, thank God! Will Britney take the Grace Kelly route and one day become a princess? Only time will tell!

Really what Britney needs is a guy who shares her interests and values. The southern singing star of the Backstreet Boys would have been a good choice. Neither Britney nor **Brian Littrell** like to party all night long. And they're both devout in their religions. They could stay at home and read the Bible together. Oh, well, too bad he's engaged . . . Of course, he ain't married yet!

Let's face it. If Britney could date anyone famous, it would be **Ben Affleck.** She's loved him forever and would just die to go out with him. She actually had lunch with him once, but it really wasn't a date because she dragged one of her friends along. At the time of this writing, Britney's reviewing a script for a role in a movie opposite Ben Affleck. Just hang on, girlfriend. Hundreds of Hollywood romances have been sparked on a movie set! Could this be her big chance?

Will Britney ever have time for romance?

Quiz 10

Cool shades, dude! (Britney collects 'em.)

Almost There!

1. **Britney's brother Bryan is engaged to be married. What's Britney's soon-to-be-sister-in-law's name?**
a. Sally Sue
b. Blaize
c. Tiffany
d. Debbie Lee

2. **What is Britney's favorite baseball team?**
a. The New York Yankees
b. The Baltimore Orioles
c. The Boston Red Sox
d. The Toronto Blue Jays

3. **Which film was shot in the same high school as Britney's video "...Baby, One More Time"?**
a. *The Breakfast Club*
b. *Sixteen Candles*
c. *Loser*
d. *Grease*

4. **Where was the video for "...Baby, One More Time" shot?**
a. Venice High School
b. Rydell High School
c. Paul D. Schreiber High School
d. Saint Mary's High School

5. **Who is Britney's favorite songwriter?**
a. Elton John
b. Max Martin
c. Diane Warren
d. Brian Littrell

6. **What's Britney's favorite flower?**
a. White roses
b. Daisies
c. Purple mums
d. Black-eyed Susans

7. **If Brit could live anywhere in the world—not counting anywhere in Louisiana so she can be close to her family—where would it be?**
a. Florida
b. New York
c. Arizona
d. Hawaii

8. **What are Brit's fave foods?**
a. Pasta and hot dogs
b. Pizza and burgers
c. Peanut butter and jelly
d. Chocolate chip cookies and chocolate milk

9. **What kind of braces did Britney have on her teeth?**
a. All metal, like train tracks!
b. Braces with a single wire
c. Clear braces
d. None—she never had braces

10. **Who is Brit's fave Backstreet Boy?**
a. A.J. McLean
b. Nick Carter
c. Howie Dorough
d. Kevin Richardson

11. **Which of the following products is Britney a spokesperson for:**
a. Herbal Essences
b. Polaroid
c. Tommy Hilfiger
d. All of the above

12. **If Britney could be any animal at all, what would it be?**
a. A kitten
b. A puppy dog
c. A soaring bird
d. A shark

13. **If Britney had a chance to sing with one artist, who would it be?**
a. Dave Matthews
b. Michael Jackson
c. Madonna
d. Steve Perry of Journey

14. **What's Britney's fave sport?**
a. Ice hockey
b. Basketball
c. Tennis
d. Football

15. **Where was Britney's favorite "concert hall" as a little girl?**
a. The kitchen table
b. The family room—in front of the TV
c. The bathroom
d. The backyard patio

ANSWERS

1. b
2. a
3. d
4. a
5. c
6. a
7. d
8. a
9. c
10. c
11. b
12. b
13. c
14. b
15. c

SCORING

*Give yourself one point for every question you answered correctly. Now, give yourself **three extra points** each if you got 4, 5, and 10 right.*

QUIZ #10 SCORE: _____

Britney poses with a radio award in London.

When Britney sings, fireworks go off!

Britney: Fact or Fiction?

Quiz 11

1. Britney is getting a road sign on I-95, in Louisiana, marking the state as the home of Britney Spears.

2. There's a statue of Britney Spears on Bourbon Street, right in the heart of New Orleans.

3. Britney once slipped on a cupcake during a performance.

4. Britney has never been involved in an air disaster.

5. Britney was the most popular girl in her school.

6. Lynne Spears always pushed her daughter into beauty pageants.

7. Britney had never met the person who beat her in *Star Search* before appearing on the show.

8. Britney had won a film role at the same time she auditioned for *MMC*.

9. Britney worked all through the school year, but like every other kid, she had her summers to herself to have fun shopping, swimming, or whatever she wanted.

10. Britney's mentioned in Eminem's song "The Real Slim Shady."

11. Britney's favorite saying is "A bird in the hand is worth two in the bush."

12. Britney was once in an all-girl band.

13. For her audition for Jive, Britney made a demo tape of a song called "Today," which had been cut from a Toni Braxton album.

14. Britney worked with Eminem to create a song that combined his "The Real Slim Shady" with her "Oops ... I Did It Again."

15. Britney hates girl groups and wants nothing to do with them at all.

Part 5

How could Eminem dis our Britney? What a jerk!

ANSWERS

1. Fiction. She is getting a sign—but on I-55!

2. Fiction—or at least not yet!

3. Fact.

4. Fiction—believe it or not! In 1998, Britney's plane had to make an emergency landing on her way from New York to Nashville with fellow recording artist Don Philips. No wonder the poor gal's afraid to fly. Who could blame her?!?

5. Fiction. While Britney had friends, she says she generally "did my own thing."

6. Fiction. Lynne entered Britney in one beauty pageant and after hearing the other mothers tell their daughters that their looks were the most important thing, she never entered Britney in another.

7. Fiction. She knew him from The Professional Children's School in New York.

8. Fact. Around the same time Britney auditioned for *MMC* the second time, she also auditioned for a movie called *Gordy*. She was offered the lead part playing opposite a pig. She passed on the offer because she was waiting to hear from the *MMC*.

9. Fiction. Britney spent summers in New York and attended the Off-Broadway Dance Center and the Professional Performing Arts School while her pals back home hung out at the mall and went swimming!

10. Fact.

11. Fiction. It's really: "Live each day to the fullest as if it were your last."

12. Fact.

13. Fact.

14. Fiction—the song exists but you can be sure Britney had nothing to do with it!

15. Fiction. Innosense, the girl group that Brit was in for all of one day, has opened for some of Britney's concerts. Britney has also opened for B*witched.

SCORING

*Give yourself one point for every question you answered correctly. Now, give yourself **three extra points** each if you got 1, 6, and 15 right.*

QUIZ #11 SCORE: _____

"You drive me cray-zay!"

Finish

Quiz 12

that Line—Part 2

1. "Lost in an image, in a dream, But there's no one there to wake her up…"

2. "Love is the first thing, last thing on our minds…"

3. "Heart, all the hurt will soon be gone, If you, if you just keep on beating strong…"

4. "You tell me you're in love with me…"

5. "I love all the ways that you show me you'll never leave…"

6. "We're monster riding to the music tonight…"

7. "Time will take us apart that's true…"

8. "But you smile and the words they tell me quickly disappear…"

9. "Some people search what seems to be a lifetime, To find a love like this…"

10. "All day and night I just dream of you (of you)…"

11. "I used to go with the flow, Didn't really care 'bout me…"

12. "She's the great gift, a gift of spring…"

13. "Don't go knockin' on my door, Gotta stay away for sure…"

14. "You promised yourself, but to somebody else, And you made it so perfectly clear…"

15. "I don't wanna hear that I'm too young, To know it's love that makes me feel this way…"

Britney Spears, pop princess.

ANSWERS

1. "...And the world is spinning, and she keeps on winning, But tell me what happens when it stops?" ("Lucky")

2. "...Run to love until the end of time" ("The Beat Goes On")

3. "...You will always be my friend, So keep on hanging in, And we'll find love again" ("Heart")

4. "...That you can't take your pretty eyes away from me" ("Sometimes")

5. "...And the way your kisses, they always convince me, Your feelings run so deep" ("When Your Eyes Say It")

6. "...A clever way to get by" ("Soda Pop")

7. "...But I will always be there for you" ("I Will Still Love You")

8. "...You speak and there's no other voice that I can hear" ("Thinkin' About You")

9. "...And here we are, With everything we wished for, I never felt such bliss" ("Deep In My Heart")

10. "...I think about all the things that we could do" ("I'm So Curious")

11. "...You might think that I can't take it, but you're wrong" ("Stronger")

12. "...You just enjoy watching—she will dance and sing" ("My Little Star," Lynne Spears' poem about Britney, the toddler)

13. "...You say you miss me like crazy now, But I ain't buyin' that" ("Don't Go Knockin' on My Door")

14. "...Still I wish you were here" ("From the Bottom of My Broken Heart")

15. "...'Cause I don't have to feel the heat of the sun, To know it's shining on me every day" ("One Kiss From You")

SCORING

*Give yourself one point for every question you answered correctly. Now, give yourself **three extra points** each if you got 2, 8, and 12 right.*

QUIZ #12 SCORE: _____

Brit signs a CD for an adoring older fan—sure, it's for your daughter!

Britney singles out a "Lucky" fan during a performance.

for the

You just can't get enough Britney!

Love of Britney

Just what wouldn't Britney's fans do to get close to their favorite princess of pop? Britney's fans go wild—not to mention their parents! What would you do to get tickets to a Britney Spears concert?

Would you eat 104 earthworms? One devoted father did! And in the same Louisiana competition, another performed a striptease, while many other parents tried out other stunts—all in the hopes of getting tickets for their kids. The winners of this contest actually paraded around in costume, the dad as Britney and the mom as a baby with a giant baby bottle, which she used to hit him when he sang, "Hit me, baby, one more time." Can you imagine your folks in that getup? Sheesh!

Britney: Fact or Fiction?

Quiz 13

1. Britney takes being called a young Madonna as an insult.

2. When Britney was a kid, she wore braces and a retainer that she refers to as "huge and obnoxious."

3. Britney is great friends with Danielle Fishel of *Boy Meets World*.

4. The famous *Rolling Stone* photos were taken on sets in a photographer's studio.

5. Britney is two years older than her cousin, Laura Lynne.

6. There are a lot of girls in Britney's family.

7. Britney is a big fan of the World Wrestling Federation (WWF).

8. Britney would never date a fan.

9. Britney has never smoked a cigarette.

10. Britney won a best attendance award at the Renee Donewar School of Dance.

11. Britney is madly in love with *NSYNC'er Justin Timberlake.

12. In twenty years, Britney would like to have three kids and just be a mom.

13. Britney has a teacup Yorkshire terrier named Francie.

14. Britney hurt her knee during the filming of the video for "Oops...I Did It Again."

15. Britney loved her gymnastic lessons.

Part 6

"Sometimes I run, sometimes I hide"
...sometimes I just dance around!

ANSWERS

1. Fiction. Britney loves everything about Madonna, and being compared to her is a high compliment.

2. Absolutely a fact.

3. Fact.

4. Fiction. Those shots were taken at her home and around her hometown.

5. Fiction. Britney is older, but Britney's aunt Sandra was pregnant with Laura Lynne when Britney was born.

6. Fiction. It was all boys until Britney and Laura Lynne came along!

7. Fact.

8. Fiction. If Britney really liked him, she'd definitely date him.

9. Fiction. Britney smoked a cigarette for a *Saturday Night Live* sketch. But don't expect Britney to pick up that bad habit. When asked how she liked it she said, "It was horrible but I didn't inhale."

10. Fact. Brit has admitted she would cry if she ever had to miss a class.

11. Fiction. While it's a fact that she has kissed Justin, they are just friends. Britney just doesn't have time for a steady boyfriend.

12. Fact.

13. Fiction. Yes, Brit has a teacup Yorkshire terrier—but her name is Mitzi!

14. Fiction. But she was hit on the head by a camera and needed four stitches!

15. Fiction. While she excelled as a gymnast, Britney was much happier devoting her time to her dance lessons.

SCORING

*Give yourself one point for every question you answered correctly. Now, give yourself **three extra points** each if you got 4, 7, and 13 right.*

QUIZ #13 SCORE: _____

Has Britney replaced Justin to become the newest member of *NSYNC?

THE

Quiz 14

1. Where is Lynne Spears' mother (Brit's grandma) originally from?
a. Louisiana
b. Alabama
c. Canada
d. England

2. What kind of car does Britney drive?
a. A Porsche
b. A Trans-Am
c. A Mercedes
d. A Volkswagen

3. What's Britney's shoe size?
a. 5
b. 6
c. 7
d. 8

4. What was the first concert Britney ever went to?
a. New Kids on the Block
b. Nirvana
c. Duran Duran
d. Boyz II Men

5. What's Britney's worst habit?
a. She picks her nose
b. She picks her toenails
c. She picks her ears
d. She picks her scabs

Britney says it's time for Quiz 14!

LAST LAP

6. What's Britney's favorite football team?

a. The Washington Redskins

b. The New Orleans Saints

c. The Atlanta Falcons

d. The New York Giants

7. What's the most important thing in the world to Britney?

a. God

b. Her family

c. Happiness

d. All of the above

8. What's Britney's favorite song from *Oops!...I Did It Again*?

a. "Stronger"

b. "Satisfaction"

c. "Lucky"

d. "Dear Diary"

9. What position did Britney play when she played basketball in middle school?

a. Forward

b. Point guard

c. Center

d. All of the above

10. What's Britney's favorite ride at Disney World?

a. The Rockin' Roller Coaster

b. The Pirates of the Caribbean

c. Peter Pan

d. She prefers Epcot Center

11. If Britney could change anything in her life, what would it be?

a. She'd make more money

b. She'd have a steady boyfriend

c. She'd get more sleep

d. She'd stop performing live

12. What is Britney's poodle's name?

a. Lady

b. Tramp

c. Curley

d. Moe

13. Britney says the most memorable moment in her life was when:

a. She finally made it into *MMC*

b. Her little sister was born

c. Her first single went to number one

d. She saw the video for "...Baby, One More Time" on MTV

14. How frequent were Britney's gymnastic lessons?

a. Once a week for an hour

b. Twice a week for an hour

c. Four days a week for two hours

d. Five days a week for three hours

15. Where did Britney take gymnastic lessons?

a. In Covington

b. In New Orleans

c. In Kentwood

d. In Mississippi

ANSWERS

1. d
2. c
3. b
4. d
5. b
6. c
7. d
8. a
9. b
10. a
11. c
12. a
13. b
14. d
15. a

SCORING

*Give yourself one point for every
question you answered correctly.
Now, give yourself **three extra points**
each if you got 1, 5, and 13 right.*

QUIZ #14 SCORE: _____

Britney gave up gymnastics when she
was pretty young, but the way she flips
around, it's like she never stopped!

Britney: Fact or Fiction?

Quiz 15

1. Britney is a slave to fashion and insists on wearing nothing but the top designer labels.

2. Britney needed surgery because she had a piece of bone floating in her knee.

3. Britney was a colicky, cranky baby!

4. Britney's mom teaches preschool.

5. Britney has appeared in several national commercials.

6. Britney spent three summers in New York before making it big.

7. It has been rumored that Britney is romantically involved with Justin Timberlake of *NSYNC.

8. Britney's appearance in *Rolling Stone* prompted the Mississippi-based American Family Association, a media watchdog group, to start a Britney boycott.

9. Britney has a picture of Brad Pitt on her refrigerator that she kisses every morning.

10. If Britney had her choice, her name would be "Madison Spears."

11. For Christmas 1999, Britney bought her father a new car.

12. Britney hates the WB show *Dawson's Creek*.

13. Britney has never gotten online to chat with fans.

14. Britney takes home-study high school courses through the correspondence program of the University of Nebraska.

15. Guys are always chatting up Britney at parties.

Part 7

Britney on a boating trip.

ANSWERS

1. Fiction. While Britney's a fashion maven, she never misses out on a good bargain. Clothing labels don't mean much to her because growing up her family didn't have much money. Brit became an expert at finding great clothes on the sales racks!

2. Fact.

3. Fiction. According to Lynne Spears, Britney was very sweet and lovable.

4. Fiction. While she ran a preschool when Brit was growing up, Lynne is currently a second-grade teacher.

5. Fact.

6. Fact.

7. Fact.

8. Fact.

9. Fact.

10. Fact. She's also partial to "Alana"!

11. Fiction. She bought him a stainless-steel outdoor grill.

12. Fiction. It's one of her favorite shows. And while plans for her to join the cast for a couple of shows didn't quite work out, she doesn't hold a grudge. Brit still catches it whenever she can!

13. Fiction. Britney has actually tried to chat with fans online, but no one believed it was her! In fact, there were even a couple of people in the chat room at the same time pretending to be Britney!

14. Fact.

15. Fiction. Britney says her fame intimidates guys. "Do you think they come up to me at parties and chitchat? No. They don't really say anything and act kind of shy."

SCORING

*Give yourself one point for every question you answered correctly. Now, give yourself **three extra points** each if you got 1, 7, and 12 right.*

QUIZ #15 SCORE: _____

Everywhere she goes, Brit makes new friends: girls, guys, dolphins...

1981

- Britney is born on December 2, the first daughter of Jamie and Lynne Spears

1982

- Laura Lynne Covington, Brit's cousin and lifelong friend, is born

1984

- Britney begins dance lessons at the Renee Donewar School of Dance in Kentwood, Louisiana

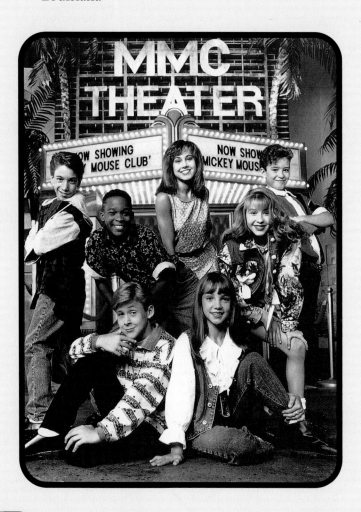

1988

- Britney competes in a talent competition and wins
- Britney competes in her first and last beauty pageant

1989

- Britney begins gymnastics lessons in Covington, Louisiana

1990

- In August, Britney wins her first competition at the Bellmont in Baton Rouge
- Britney wins the Miss Talent USA competition
- Britney auditions for the *All-New Mickey Mouse Club* but doesn't get in
- Britney spends the first of three summers in New York studying at The Professional Children's School and the Broadway Dance Center
- Britney lands the part of Tina in *Ruthless*, an off-Broadway show
- Britney auditions for a movie called *Gordy* and wins the leading role opposite a pig, but declines the offer
- Britney auditions a second time for the *All-New Mickey Mouse Club* and lands a part on the show

1991

- Britney quits gymnastics to focus on dance. She tours around Louisiana competing in both group and solo dance competitions
- Britney appears on *Star Search* and wins with three and three-quarters stars. She loses the next round, however, to an opera-singing kid

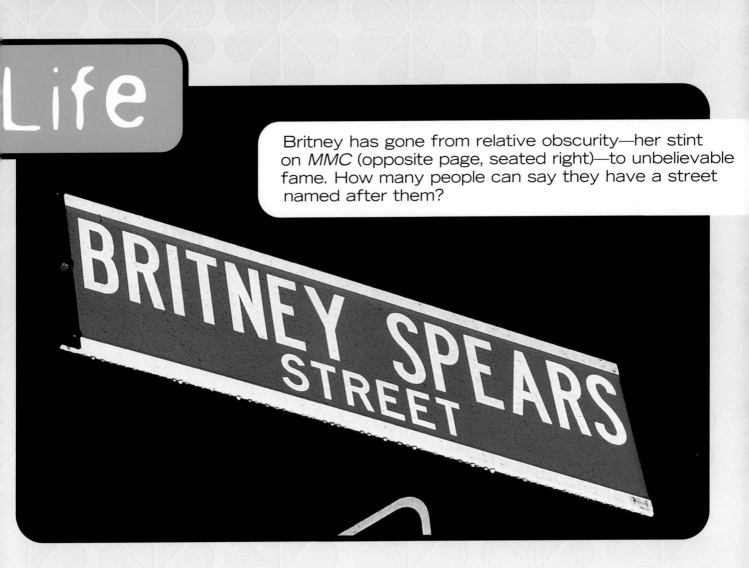

Britney has gone from relative obscurity—her stint on *MMC* (opposite page, seated right)—to unbelievable fame. How many people can say they have a street named after them?

1993–1994

• Britney appears on Disney's *All-New Mickey Mouse Club* for two seasons
• Britney joins the all-girl group Innosense but soon quits in hopes of a solo career

1997

• Britney is signed to Jive Records

1998

• Britney performs at shopping malls three months before her first single's release in October
• Britney tours with *NSYNC for two months.
• Britney models clothing for Tommy Hilfiger's spring 1999 collection

1999

• Britney is the first female and youngest artist ever to have a simultaneous number-one debut album and single
• Britney's album …*Baby, One More Time* is simultaneously certified gold, platinum, and double-platinum
• In March, Britney appears in a provocative spread in *Rolling Stone* and becomes the center of a big controversy
• Britney's official website is launched on August 30, www.britneyspears.com

2000

• Britney wins favorite new pop-rock artist of 1999 at the American Music Awards
• *Britney Spears' Heart to Heart* hits bookstores
• Felicia Culotta's *Britney Spears Scrapbook* comes out

Quiz 16

1. Where did Britney go to elementary school?
a. St. Peter's School
b. Daly Elementary School
c. Parklane Academy
d. The Kentwood Academy for the Arts

2. How old was Britney when she gave up gymnastics?
a. Five
b. Seven
c. Nine
d. Eleven

3. What was Britney's dance specialty?
a. Jazz lyrical dancing
b. Tap
c. Ballet
d. Modern dance

4. What was one of Britney's favorite events in gymnastics?
a. Uneven bars
b. Floor exercises
c. Both a and b
d. Neither a nor b—she liked the balance beam best

Britney leans on the car used in the "Sometimes" video. At the time the video was filmed, Britney didn't have a driver's license. Now she owns a white Mercedes.

5. How much money did Britney have for lunch every day when she was in school?

a. $0.50

b. $1.00

c. $1.50

d. $2.50

6. What does Britney's dad do for a living?

a. He's a plumber

b. He's a building contractor

c. He's a mason

d. He's a TV repairman

7. Which of the following shows has Britney appeared on?

a. *The Today Show*

b. *Saturday Night Live*

c. *The Rosie O'Donnell Show*

d. All of the above

8. Which big celebrity appeared on the same episode of *The View* with Britney—and asked Britney for *her* autograph?

a. Demi Moore

b. Sigourney Weaver

c. Meg Ryan

d. Barbra Streisand

9. When did Britney's official website launch?

a. July 15, 1999

b. August 30, 1999

c. January 15, 2000

d. March 30, 2000

10. What is Britney's favorite gift from a fan?

a. A diamond engagement ring

b. A singing Britney Spears Vermont teddy bear

c. A cross necklace

d. A brand-new BMW

11. What did Britney buy her mother for her first Christmas as a superstar?

a. A white Mercedes sedan

b. A new refrigerator

c. A swimming pool

d. A Porsche 911

12. Britney admits that she probably has too many:

a. Shoes

b. Crop tops

c. Pairs of sunglasses

d. Fans

13. Approximxately how much money did Britney earn in 1999?

a. $100,000

b. $500,000

c. $1,000,000

d. $15,000,000

14. How old was Britney when she entered her first beauty pageant?

a. Two

b. Three

c. Five

d. Six

15. How many beauty pageants has Britney been in?

a. Zero

b. One

c. Four

d. Ten

ANSWERS

1. c
2. c
3. a
4. c
5. d
6. b
7. d
8. b
9. b
10. c
11. a
12. c
13. d
14. d
15. b

SCORING

*Give yourself one point for every question you answered correctly. Now, give yourself **three extra points** each if you got 4, 8, and 13 right.*

QUIZ #16 SCORE: _____

Britney shows off one of her favorite pairs of pants.

An early concert shot.

BONUS QUIZ!

Quiz 17

1. **Fact or fiction: Britney bought a new home for her family—a four-bedroom Tudor-style gated house on seven and a half acres in her hometown of Kentwood, Louisiana.**

2. **Fact or fiction: Britney has dated Prince William.**

3. **Which band originally did the song "Satisfaction" that Britney covers on her *Oops!...I Did It Again* album?**
   a. The Who
   b. The Beatles
   c. The Ramones
   d. The Rolling Stones

4. **How many stitches did Britney need after a camera hit her in the head during the filming of her "Oops!...I Did It Again" video?**
   a. Two
   b. Four
   c. Ten
   d. Sixteen

5. **What were Britney's favorite TV shows when she was growing up?**
   a. *Fame* and *Star Search*
   b. *Growing Pains* and *The Wonder Years*
   c. *Happy Days* and *Laverne and Shirley*
   d. *Alf* and *The Cosby Show*

6. **Fact or fiction: Britney's best childhood memory is riding go-carts with her friends.**

7. **Did Britney sing a cover of "Open Arms" by Journey in concert because she's a big fan of the band?**

8. **Britney gets really upset when people cover her songs because she feels they can only be sung properly by her.**

9. **What city were the casting calls in the first time Brit auditioned for *MMC*?**
   a. New Orleans
   b. New York
   c. Omaha
   d. Atlanta

10. **How long was Britney's first ride to New York City from her hometown of Kentwood, Louisiana?**
    a. Six hours
    b. Ten hours
    c. Nineteen hours
    d. Twenty-six hours

11. **Fact or fiction: Britney doesn't really have her belly button pierced. It's a clip-on.**

12. **Fact or fiction: The first time Britney went to New York, it was just her and mom.**

13. **Fact or fiction: Britney won the "Most Likely to Succeed" distinction in her high school yearbook.**

14. **What prize did Britney make off with when she won Miss Talent USA?**
a. A check for $1,000
b. A tiara
c. A giant trophy
d. All of the above

15. **How old was Britney when she started dating regularly?**
a. Nine
b. Eleven
c. Fourteen
d. Britney has never really dated anyone

16. **Does Britney have a whole collection of her own songs she's just dying to record?**

17. **Was Britney slated to do a Paula Abdul spoof when she was the guest host on *Saturday Night Live*?**

18. **Did Eric Foster White write the song "E-mail My Heart" after watching an episode of *Beverly Hills 90210* in which Brandon sends Kelly a romantic E-mail?**

19. **Fact or fiction: Britney was offered the chance to sing "...Baby, One More Time" after the group TLC passed up the initial rights to the song.**

20. **Fact or fiction: 2gether, the mock boy band, is slated to open concerts for Britney Spears.**

Aloha, Britney!

ANSWERS

1. Fact.

2. Fiction. Britney sent Prince William a copy of her CD and some photos when she heard he was a fan. He sent back a thank-you note and an invitation to visit him the next time she was in England. The press blew this way out of proportion—into more than a flirtation.

3. d

4. b

5. b

6. Fact.

7. Yes, she did. That's a fact.

8. Fiction. In fact, Britney's a really big fan of Travis' cover of "…Baby, One More Time." As she told www.NME.com, "I was in the mall the other day and I heard this song come on and I was like 'Oh my Lordy!' It was so weird. I liked it though, I thought it was cool. It was a totally different vibe from what I did."

9. d

10. d

11. Fiction. Britney's belly button is definitely pierced, much to her mama's dismay.

12. Fiction. There was a whole entourage along for the ride: Brit's dad, brother Bryan, one of Bryan's friends, and Britney's father's sister Jeannine and her daughter Tara—Jamie Lynn wasn't born yet.

13. Fiction. While that would have been telling, no one could have predicted just how successful she would be. She was, however, voted "Most Beautiful."

14. d

15. c

16. Yes. She says she has a whole book of lyrics ready and waiting, but according to Britney, Jamie Lynn has hidden it from her somewhere. Gotta love little sisters!

17. Yes. Although the sketch was scrapped in the last rehearsal, *Teen People* magazine features a shot of Britney all costumed up and ready to go in their August 2000 issue.

18. Nope. It was actually teaching Fe how to E-mail her boyfriend that inspired him.

19. Fact.

20. Fact.

SCORING

*Give yourself one point for every question you answered correctly. Now, give yourself **three extra points** each if you got 5, 8, 10, and 17 right.*

BONUS QUIZ SCORE: _____

Britney takes a break from filming a video.

Britney shows off the gorgeous hair that landed her a stint with Herbal Essences.

Brit at the 2000 MTV Awards.

Finding

Now that you've reached the end of the book, it's time to find out just how much of a fan you are. Total up your scores for all the quizzes in the book:

Quiz #1: _____

Quiz #2: _____

Quiz #3: _____

Quiz #4: _____

Quiz #5: _____

Quiz #6: _____

Quiz #7: _____

Quiz #8: _____

Quiz #9: _____

Quiz #10: _____

Quiz #11: _____

Quiz #12: _____

Quiz #13: _____

Quiz #14: _____

Quiz #15: _____

Quiz #16: _____

Bonus Quiz: _____

Total Score: _____

Your Total Score

Are You a True-Blue Britney Spears Fan?

Compare your points below and find out!

400 + points

The hands-down winner. You are an A+ student in the subject of Britney Spears. Not only have you answered all the questions correctly, you even got all the hidden bonus points! A job well done. It's too bad you can't major in Britney Spears when you hit college—yet!

250–399 points

Not too shabby at all. You know a whole lot about Ms. Spears, and now you have the opportunity to get to know more. Reread *Britney Spears' Heart to Heart*. Reread *Britney Spears: Stylin'* (okay, you don't have to—but it's chock-full of great info). Visit the Britney Spears website daily, as new information is added every day. Maybe you can take the quiz with a few friends and work at it together. You'll be a pro in no time!

100–249 points

Okay, not bad, but there's still so much to know. Maybe you haven't had a chance yet to read the book she wrote with her mom or perhaps you need to read it again! Have you picked up her new CD yet? If not, save up that cash and get out to the record stores as soon as you have ample funds. It is an absolute must-listen! Once you've taken the proper measures, take the quizzes again and you'll be on your way to a perfect score!

99 or less points

Hmmm. You're going to need a little help with this one. There were a bunch of really easy questions in these quizzes—maybe you were daydreaming that you were one of Brit's dancers and you weren't really paying attention when you answered them. Maybe you forgot this was a quiz about Britney Spears. Or maybe you're new to the world of Britney and just getting started as a fan. In that case, check out the resource list on the next page. It will show you where you can find lots of information about Britney. Then, educate yourself and take the quizzes again!

RESOURCE

Britney Spears Fan Clubs
Britney Spears
c/o Britney Fan Club
PO Box 7022
Red Bank, NJ 07701-7022

The Britney Spears Fan Club
PO Box 250
Osyka, MS 39657

Websites
Britney Spears' own website: www.britneyspears.com
The Britney Spears website: www.peeps.com/britney
E-mail Britney at: britney@peeps.com
Other notable Britney websites:
www.101britney.com
www.britneyspears.org
www.britneyzone.com
www.sfhbs.com (That's the Society for Future Husbands of Britney Spears website!)
www.britney-spears.fsnet.co.uk/
www.britneyspears.sonicnet.com

Subscribe to the Official Britney Beat E-newsletter:
www.britneyspears.com/fan_club/fan_club.html

Magazines
Check out these magazines monthly for stories and interviews:
All-Stars
B.B.
Blast
Cosmo Girl!
Cute
Entertainment Teen
J – 14
Jane
Kickin'
Seventeen
Sixteen
Super Teen
Teen Beat
Teen Celebrity
Teen Magazine
Teen People

For an official full-color Britney fan merchandise catalog:
Call: 212-741-0818
Fax: 212-929-5188
Write: Britney Spears
         c/o Zomba Merchandise Inc.
         PO Box 1771
         New York, NY 10116-1771

Bibliography

PERIODICALS

Andrews, W.C. "Britney Spears Signs Autographs Before Concert." Knight-Ridder/Tribune News Service. (January 19, 1999).

Associated Press. "Britney Spears Museum Planned." *New York Times.* (June 24, 2000).

"Bopping Right to the Top." *Newsweek.* (April 10, 2000).

"Britney Spears." *Teen Girl Power.* (March 1999): 70.

"Britney Spears: Singer." *People Weekly.* (May 10, 1999).

Brown, Ethan. "*Teen People* Gives Newcomer Britney Spears the Cinderella Treatment and Turns Small-town Girl Into a Stunning Pop Princess." *Teen People.* (April 1999): 126-127.

Chambers, Veronica, with Gill James. "Pop's (Sexy) Teen Angel." *Newsweek.* (March 1, 1999): 64.

Cury, James Oliver. "Mouse-keteer: Guess What? Britney Spears Wants to Conquer the Web, too." *Entertainment Weekly.* (September 17, 1999).

Daly, Steven. "Britney Spears: Inside the Mind (and Bedroom) of America's New Teen Queen." *Rolling Stone.* (April 15, 1999): 60-65, 129-131.

Flick, Larry. "After Quiet Build, Jive's Teen Star Spears Breaks Out." *Billboard.* (December 12, 1998): 1.

_____. "Spears Taps Teen Spirit." *Billboard.* (December 4, 1999).

Helligar, Jeremy, with Michael Haederle. "A Major Minor: Singer Britney Spears, 17, Flexes Her Muscles in the Booming Teen Music Market." *People Weekly.* (February 15, 1999): 71.

LIST

Hit Sensations Presents Britney Spears: Britney Hits the Big Time. Hit Sensations TV Series Presents vol 1 no 22. Fanzine International, New York.

Kafka, Peter. "The Queen of Teen." *Forbes.* (March 20, 2000).

Laudadio, Marisa. "Mouthing Off." *Teen Magazine.* (March 2000).
_____. "Time Out With Britney Spears." *Teen Magazine.* (August 1999).

Lenz, Stephen. "Britney Spears." *Teen Celebrity.* (March 1999): 46.

_____. "Britney Spears: Who Better Than This Teen Phenomenon to Dish Prom Tips?" *Teen Celebrity.* (Summer 1999): 43-47.

Mayfield, Geoff, Keith Caulfield, and Steve Graybow. "Teen Queens." *Billboard.* (February 13, 1999): 116.

Mayfield, Geoff. "How Big Is Big?" *Billboard.* (May 20, 2000).

Novak, Ralph. Review, "...Baby, One More Time." *People Weekly.* (February 1, 1999).

Rice, Lynette. "On the Air: The latest news from the TV beat." *Entertainment Weekly.* (June 30, 2000).

Sanders, Heather. "From the Bottom of Her Heart." *Girl's Life.* (March 1999): 26-28.

Thiggpen, David E. "A Sweet Sensation: Killer Abs and an Army of Producers Put Britney Spears on Top. Will Fans Love Her Tomorrow?" *Time.* (March 1, 1999): 71.

Tresniowski, Alex. "Britney's Wild Ride." *People Weekly.* (February 14, 2000).

"We're All Ears for Britney Spears." *Teen Beat.* (June 1999): 37.

WORLD WIDE WEB

Boehlert, Eric. "Baby, One More Teen: 16-Year-Old Britney Spears Goes From Shopping Malls to No. 1." *Rolling Stone* Online. (January 20, 1999).

Britney Spears bio. peeps.com / bmg.com, © 1999 BMG Online.

Freydkin, Donna. "Pop Princess Britney Spears Sets Out to Conquer Music." Special to CNN Interactive. (March 24, 1999).

Graff, Gary. "Britney Spears: The Queen of the Charts Talks Candidly." *Rolling Stone* Online. (February 26, 1999).

Lanham, Tom. Review, "...Baby, One More Time." *Entertainment Weekly* Online. (January 12, 1999).

The *Rolling Stone* Online service was used to obtain the following bios: Britney Spears, Madonna, Mariah Carey, Whitney Houston, Backstreet Boys, *NSYNC.

TV Guide. Transcript of Online Chat with Britney Spears. (March 29, 1999).

Adrian Donnelly, England, authored the following articles about Britney Spears for www.101britney.com:
"Britney Spears Speaks About Her Near Death Plane Experience." July 5, 2000
"Britney Became Too Big For *Dawson's Creek*." July 5, 2000
"Britney Decides to Wear Her Sexy Outfits, Not Record Company People." July 5, 2000
"Huge NYC Crowd Watches Britney on NBC." July 5, 2000
"Britney Gets a Road Sign." July 5, 2000
"Eminem and Britney Mixing It Up." July 5, 2000
"Britney Camp Starts Soon." July 5, 2000

BOOKS

Spears, Britney and Lynne Spears. *Britney Spears' Heart to Heart.* NY: Crown Publishers, 2000.

Marron, Maggie. *Britney Spears: Stylin'.* NY: Warner Books, 1999.

PHOTO CREDITS

Britney gives a heartfelt performance for her fans.

THE ULTIMATE

BRITNEY SPEARS

QUIZ BOOK